Introdu🖢 KT-225-903

Mind-set: a fixed mental attitude.

If standing up for what you believe means you get hurt, should you still do it? Would you be brave enough? That's where this story comes from. *Mind-Set* is about people trying to do what they believe is right. The bombers, Adam, Dennis, Mark – all of them think they are in the right.

The hardest thing about turning the book *Mind-Set* into a play was the ending – the book doesn't have a proper one! It ends with Mark watching a fight, not knowing what to do. That's fine in a book, but you can't do that on stage – it doesn't feel right. I still wanted to keep the "what's he going to choose?" feeling, so I wrote two endings, showing two different choices.

Even if you do what you think is right, will your life be better because of it?

For Phil, my sounding board

Contents

Cast

Mark

Mark is 16. He isn't very good at school stuff but he likes hanging out with his mates. He and Shaleem have been friends for years, and Shaleem sometimes helps Mark with his homework.

Shaleem

Shaleem's family is from Bangladesh but he has grown up in the UK. Shaleem is very clever and is planning to be a doctor, like his dad. Shaleem likes being friends with Mark because Mark keeps him chilled out.

Adam

Adam is in the same year as Mark and Shaleem. He is strong and likes to play rugby.

Jemma

Jemma has been going out with Adam for a few months. Being with Adam makes Jemma feel strong. She likes to say what she thinks, even if it shocks other people.

Rob

Rob is an easy-going person, but he doesn't like to be different. He looks up to Adam at school because Adam says what he thinks and lots of people like him.

Mark's Mum

Mark's mum feels very alone since Mark's dad left her. She always has a boyfriend but she doesn't stand up for herself, and so most times she goes out with men who aren't very nice to her.

Dennis

Dennis is going out with Mark's mum at the moment. He thinks a woman belongs in the kitchen and he likes Mark's mum because she doesn't talk back to him.

A Note on the Performance

Jemma and Mark's mum don't appear together in the same scene. This means that one actor can play both parts, if needed. The same is true of Rob and Dennis. So, to perform this play, you need at least 5 actors.

This play has two possible endings. At the end of Scene 6, the audience is asked to choose what Mark, the main character, should do next. Scene 7 and Scene 8 play out the two choices – you perform one or the other, not both.

Scene 1

School Classroom

It is the afternoon. The lights are all on in the classroom. There is a white board and a teacher's desk at one end of the room. There are displays of students' work pinned up on the walls.

(The bell rings. Mark, Shaleem, Adam and Rob walk into the classroom. They are all in a good mood.)

Mark: You could have helped me out, Shaleem. Given me a hint. Call yourself a friend?

(Shaleem grins at Mark.)

Shaleem: But that would be cheating.
Don't blame me for your
grade. You didn't revise.

Mark: I was busy, OK?

Adam: So what did you get,
Shaleem?

Mark: He got an A star. Of course.

(Adam puts his hands up and pretends to bow down to Shaleem.)

Adam: Doctor Shaleem.

(Rob joins in with Adam and bows down to Shaleem.)

Rob: We are not worthy.

Shaleem: Oh, shut up. You could all do that well if you put some effort into it.

Rob: Nah, mate. It's in the blood, innit? I mean, your dad's a doctor. Mine runs a fish and chip shop.

Mark: My dad drives a lorry.

Adam: Yeah, and my dad drives a Tube train. Round and round all day. You don't need brains to do that.

Rob: There you are, see? You've got brain-box blood.

Shaleem: Oh, leave it out.

(Jemma, Adam's girlfriend, walks into the classroom and goes over to Adam.)

Adam: Hi, sexy.

Jemma: Hi, babe.

Rob: I think I'm gonna puke.

(Shaleem and Mark move over to some desks on the other side of the classroom.)

Mark: Rob's got a point, Shaleem. You were born clever. I never know why you hang around with me.

Shaleem: Because you're my friend, Mark. That's why.

Mark: But we're nothing like each other. You're always on time for everything – I'm always late. You're always top of the class. I'm so far from the top I can't even see it.

Shaleem: What is this, you trying to make me feel sorry for you or something? We're mates, Mark. We've always been mates. We'll always be mates. That's just how it is. Why have you got to worry about it?

Mark: Yeah, you're right. Sorry. Dunno what came over me. Must be all this "talking about feelings" crap we do in PSHE.

Shaleem: You scared me there for a moment. Thought you were turning into a girl.

(*Mark gives Shaleem a push with his elbow. At the same time, Adam's mobile phone rings.*)

Adam: Yeah? Yeah, Mum, it's me, who else would it be? You OK? You sound weird.

(*Adam suddenly goes silent. He freezes as he listens to his Mum on the phone.*)

Jemma: Come on, babe. I have to go to my locker before Maths.

(*Adam drops his mobile and runs out of the room.*)

Jemma: Adam? Babe?

(Jemma runs out after Adam. Rob picks up Adam's mobile from the floor.)

Rob: What was all that about?

(At that moment, there is a message read out by the Head Teacher over the intercom.)

Head Teacher: Pay attention, all staff and students. This is a very important message. A number of bombs have been set off on the Underground in London. It is thought that lots of people may be hurt or trapped. I know many of you have family who work in London, so you will want to

12

call to make sure they are all right. If you don't have a phone, you can call from the school office.

(Mark, Shaleem and Rob look at each other in shock.)

Head Teacher: The school will close for the rest of the day. If there is no one at home to look after you, you must stay here. If there is someone at home, please report out to your form teacher before you go. Do not leave school without reporting out. School will

open as normal tomorrow.

(The intercom ends with a crackle.)

Mark: Bloody hell.

(Shaleem pulls out his mobile.)

Shaleem: I gotta call my dad. He's

working at the hospital in

King's Cross today.

Mark: For once I'm glad my dad's a

lorry driver.

Rob: I've got no credit on my

phone. It'll be faster for me

to run home than try to
ring from the office. And I'll
drop Adam's phone off at his
house, too.

Mark: Didn't Adam say his dad
drives a Tube train?

Rob: Yeah. Things could be bad.
See you tomorrow.

*(Rob leaves the classroom. Shaleem is
talking on his mobile.)*

Shaleem: Dad? Oh, I see. No, it's
Shaleem. Can you page him
for me? No, I don't need to
speak to him. I just wanted

to make sure he's OK. Yeah,
I just heard. How bad is it?
Oh, I see. Thanks.

(Shaleem puts his mobile into his pocket. He turns to speak to Mark.)

Shaleem: There were three bombs,
Mark. In the middle of rush
hour. How could anyone do
that?

Mark: Jeez. I'd better get home.

Shaleem: Me too. See you later.

Scene 2

The Kitchen in Mark's House

The kitchen is very tidy. The mugs are in a neat line on the side by the kettle and the sink is spotless. Above the sink there is a window that looks out onto a small, empty garden.

(Mark's mum is sitting at the table with a mug of tea. Mark comes in and drops his school bag on the floor by the door.)

Mark: Mum! I didn't think you'd be here.

Mum:	What are you doing back so early?
Mark:	School's closed. 'Cos of the bombs. Why aren't you at work?
Mum:	My boss knows someone who was hurt. He closed the shop early, so I got the afternoon off.
Mark:	So what's going on?
Mum:	God, it's awful, Mark. I've been watching the news on TV. They reckon something

like fifty people are dead.
And hundreds more hurt.

Mark: Who did it?

Mum: No one knows yet. But
they're saying it was an
Islamic group.

Mark: A what group?

Mum: Islamic. You know –
Muslims. People who believe
in the Islamic religion.

Mark: Like Shaleem.

Mum:	The bombers blew themselves up at the same time, whoever they were.
Mark:	Jeez. Why?
Mum:	I don't know, do I? To die for something they believe in, I guess.
Mark:	That's stupid.
Mum:	Not to them.
Mark:	Shaleem was worried about his dad, but he's OK. Thank God Dad's in France at the moment.

Mum: Is he? I wouldn't know.

Mark: You could at least make an effort.

Mum: What for? It was over a long time ago, Mark. Let's not go through this again.

Mark: You never gave him a chance.

Mum: I gave him plenty of chances! He just threw them away, that's all. Couldn't keep his hands off other women. I don't have to put up with

that. I can do better than
him.

Mark: Like Dennis?

Mum: Listen, Mark, you may not
like Dennis but he's been
good to me. Treats me well.
He doesn't mess me around
like your dad. I know where
I am with Dennis.

Mark: Yeah, under his thumb.

Mum: What would you know about
it? It's nothing to do with
you anyway.

Mark:	But –
Mum:	No, Mark, I'm not going to discuss it with you. Besides, Dennis is coming over for dinner tomorrow and I want you to be polite to him.
Mark:	I'll be out.
Mum:	You will not. You will be here for dinner and you'll behave yourself, or else.

(Mark rolls his eyes and mutters to himself.)

Mark:	Can't wait.

Scene 3

School Classroom

The classroom is full. Everyone is waiting for the teacher to turn up. Mark and Shaleem are sitting next to each other. Adam and Rob are sitting on the other side of the room, talking in low voices and looking over at Shaleem.

Mark: Miss Patto's away today.

Shaleem: Maybe we'll have a supply teacher.

Mark: Hope so. Then we can doss about.

Shaleem: You doss about in PSHE
anyway.

Mark: True.

*(Mark looks over to Adam and Rob and
frowns. Then he turns to Shaleem.)*

Mark: What are those two talking
about?

Shaleem: Dunno.

Mark: They keep looking at you.

Shaleem: Have I got something on my
face?

Mark: Yeah, your nose.

(Mark and Shaleem laugh. Jemma comes into the classroom. She is holding a pile of work sheets for the PSHE lesson.)

Jemma: They forgot about us so we haven't got a teacher. But Mr Martin's next door and he says he'll come in if we're too loud. We've got to do a quiz but we can work in groups.

Mark: Told you it would be a doss.

(Jemma hands out the sheets to everyone in the room.)

Mark: So what's the quiz about?

(Shaleem reads the sheet out loud.)

Shaleem: "Your hopes and dreams for the coming years."

Mark: Oh, great. Another lame topic.

Shaleem: Question One. "What do you see as the greatest danger to people's way of life in the years to come?"

Mark: Bad dress sense.

Shaleem: Mark, it's not a joke.

Mark:	Oh, don't be a square. It's only a stupid quiz. Why, what are you putting?
Shaleem:	Cancer.
Rob:	Crime.
Adam:	Terrorism.
Jemma:	Muslims.
Shaleem:	Muslims? You can't put that.
Jemma:	I can put what I like, it's my quiz sheet.
Shaleem:	What have you got against Muslims?

Mark: Leave it, Shaleem.

Shaleem: No way. Go on, tell me.

Jemma: Muslims put the bombs on the Tube. It's because of them that fifty people are dead. It's because of them that Adam's dad is in hospital.

Shaleem: I'm really sorry.

Adam: Yeah. His back's broken. They say he may never walk again. And it's all because of Muslims.

Jemma: Like 9/11. They were Muslims too.

Adam: That's why I've put terrorism on my quiz.

Jemma: Muslims – terrorists. Same thing.

Shaleem: Not all terrorists are Muslim. And not all Muslims are terrorists.

Jemma: But Muslims believe it's OK to kill non-Muslims. Their religion says so.

Shaleem:	No, it doesn't. Islam doesn't teach anything like that. I should know.
Adam:	You would say that. But I've seen those Muslim leaders on TV. Ranting about the West and how they hate it. How we should all be wiped out. And how bombers who kill themselves go to heaven, or whatever you call it.
Rob:	Yeah. I've seen them too.
Shaleem:	They're just mad. And no one who knows anything

about Islam listens to them anyway.

Adam: Yeah? Then how come three Muslims blew themselves up yesterday?

Jemma: I bet you think it was a good idea, don't you?

Shaleem: What? Of course I don't!

Jemma: But you believe in all that stuff. Islam. You're a Muslim – you're one of them.

Mark: What are you talking about?

Adam:	They're working to bring us down. The British way of life. My dad says so.
Rob:	So does mine.
Mark:	You're talking crap. Shaleem's not working to bring anyone down. And what about his dad? He's a doctor, not a terrorist.
Jemma:	It's not what you do, it's what you believe in.
Shaleem:	And I believe everyone has the right to free speech, but you're way out of line.

Jemma: Can't take the truth?

Mark: I think you're all nuts.

Adam: They're the ones behind all the mess in this country right now. Him and his kind.

Shaleem: My *kind?* I'm a person, just like you.

Adam: You're not like me. You're not even British.

Mark: Course he is. He's got a British passport – I've seen it.

Jemma: Don't be stupid. That doesn't
            make him British.

Mark: Doesn't it?

Shaleem: Oh, leave it, Mark. You
            won't change their minds.

Mark: But they're wrong.

Shaleem: I don't need you to fight my
            battles for me.

Jemma: No, you've got bombers to do
            that, haven't you?

*(Shaleem doesn't know what to say.
Everyone goes silent. The stage goes dark.)*

Scene 4

The Kitchen in Mark's House

There is a pan heating up on the cooker and a light is on in the oven. Next to the cooker is a tray with three steaks on it, ready to go into the oven. A chopping board is by the sink, with a sharp knife on it. There is a small fridge in one corner.

(Mark and his mum are sitting at the kitchen table.)

Mum: That's awful, what they said. I suppose I can see why Adam would be upset. His

dad being hurt so badly and
everything.

Mark: Doesn't make him right,
though, does it?

Mum: I guess not. Your teacher
should have stopped it.

Mark: We didn't have one. Miss
Patto was away.

Mum: So no one was checking up
on you? God, the state of
your school, Mark. I'd send
you to a different one if I
could.

Mark: All my friends are there. Besides, Mr Martin was just next door.

Mum: That's not good enough.

(The front door-bell rings. Mum gets up.)

Mum: That'll be Dennis.

Mark: Oh, great ...

Mum: Now, you're to behave yourself. Remember, you promised.

Mark: No, I didn't. You told me to.

Mum: Lay the table, there's a good boy.

(Mark's mum goes out of the room to open the front door.)

Mark: Stupid Dennis. Stupid dinner.

(Mark gets up and pulls open a drawer to get some knives and forks. Mum and Dennis come into the kitchen. Dennis has his arm around Mum, who looks happy. Dennis speaks to Mark.)

Dennis: All right?

Mark: Yeah.

Dennis: Chatty as ever.

Mark: What?

Dennis: Nothing. So, what we having
               for dinner, then?

Mum: Steak and chips. Your
               favourite.

Dennis: You are a goddess. Anyone
               ever tell you that?

Mum: Once or twice.

Dennis: Come here, sweet lips.

*(Mark pulls a face and pretends he's going to
be sick.)*

Dennis:	Your manners haven't improved, I see.

(Mark's mum gives Mark a look and speaks to him in a hard voice.)

Mum:	Mark ...

Mark:	Yeah, yeah. Sorry.

(Dennis sits down at the table.)

Dennis:	So what about these bombs, then?

Mum:	Awful.

Dennis:	I tell you, babe, the world's not a safe place any more.

Look at this country. Knife crime, ASBOs, teenage drinking. And now bloody Muslims come in and blow us up. After all this country's done for them!

(Mark mutters to himself so that Dennis can't hear him.)

Mark: Oh, here we go …

Dennis: The government's been too soft on people coming into this country. Refugees or asylum-seekers or whatever they're called. And now look

what's happened. It's time
to stop letting just anyone
into the country. You gotta
look after number one these
days. Look out for yourself.

Mark: What about people who need
help?

Dennis: Who cares about them?
Where's my beer?

Mum: Sorry, love. Here you go.

*(Mark's mum gets a can of beer from the
fridge and passes it to Dennis. Then she puts
the tray of steaks in the oven.)*

Dennis:	It's this wacky religion – Islam, or whatever you call it. Turns them all crazy. Tells them it's OK to kill anyone they don't like.
Mark:	No, it doesn't. Islam doesn't say anything like that.
Dennis:	Yeah? And how would you know?
Mark:	Shaleem told me.
Dennis:	Shaleem? Who the hell's Shaleem?
Mark:	My friend from school.

Dennis: Oh, him. I know who you mean. The Muslim.

Mark: Don't say it like that.

Dennis: You'd better be careful.

Mark: What do you mean?

Dennis: You can't trust people like that. They're all the same.

Mark: People like what?

Dennis: Corner-shop people. You know – Patels and Singhs and names like that. Pakistanis.

Mark:	Shaleem's not from Pakistan, he's from Bangladesh.
Dennis:	So what? He's still one of them. Coming over here and taking our jobs. Living off our job-seekers' money. Calling themselves British.
Mark:	Shaleem's dad isn't on the dole. He's a doctor. And a really good one.
Dennis:	But I bet there were British doctors who could have had that job.

Mark:	There aren't enough doctors in Britain, or didn't you know?
Dennis:	Are you calling me a liar?
Mum:	Mark ...
Mark:	No, Mum! Shaleem's my friend. I'm not having him say stuff like that.
Dennis:	I'll say what I bloody well like. Your Shaleem's bad news. You stay away from kids like that if you know what's good for you.

Mark:	You're nuts. You don't know the first thing about him!
Dennis:	Don't you speak to me like that!
Mark:	He's my mate. He's always been my mate, he'll always be my mate! It's no wonder Muslims hate the West if it's full of people like you!
Dennis:	Why, you little tosser!

(Dennis gets up and lifts his hand as if he is going to hit Mark.)

Dennis:	I'll teach you some manners!

Mum: Mark!

Mark: No need, Mum. I'm going. I couldn't sit here and eat with him anyway. And by the way ...

(Mark sniffs.)

Mark: ... your steaks are burning.

(Mark walks out, slamming the door behind him.)

Scene 5

School Classroom

Through the open door to the classroom you can see a corridor.

(Mark is waiting in the corridor. Adam and Jemma walk past him, giving him the evil eye. Mark goes to speak to them, but Adam and Jemma ignore him and go into the classroom. The bell rings. Mark looks at his watch. Rob walks in.)

Mark: Hey, Rob.

(Rob looks around to see if anyone is near by.)

Rob: Oh. Hey.

Mark: You haven't seen Shaleem,
                    have you?

Rob: Who? Uh – no.

Mark: It's so weird. He's never
                    late.

Rob: Yeah.

(Rob starts to go into the classroom.)

Mark: Hey, wait up!

Rob: Look, Mark, just leave it, OK?

Mark: Leave what?

Rob:	We all know whose side you're on.
Mark:	What are you talking about?

(Rob doesn't reply but goes into the classroom. Shaleem enters, with his hood pulled over his face.)

Mark:	Shaleem! There is something way out weird going on today. And how come you're late? You're never late!
Shaleem:	Just got a bit held up, that's all. Are we going in or what?

Mark: You'll have to put your hood down. You know how Mr Jones gets.

Shaleem: Yeah, yeah. In a bit.

Mark: What's the matter with your face?

Shaleem: Nothing.

Mark: Put your hood down.

Shaleem: No, I –

(Mark pulls down Shaleem's hood. Shaleem has a black eye.)

Mark: God! What happened?

Shaleem:	Nothing, I told you.
Mark:	Who hit you?
Shaleem:	Dunno.
Mark:	You must know! Was it Adam?
Shaleem:	Didn't see anyone, OK? Come on, we're late for class.

(Shaleem goes into the classroom. After a moment, Mark follows him. As Mark enters the room, Adam, Rob and Jemma start to make a hissing noise. The seat next to Shaleem is free, but as Mark moves towards

it slowly, the hissing noise gets louder. When Mark takes a step away from it, the hissing gets softer.)

(Mark stands there for a few moments, not knowing what to do. Shaleem looks right at him, but after a moment, Mark looks down at the floor. Then he takes a seat at another table, away from Shaleem. The hissing stops. Mark leans forward and rests his head on the table as the stage goes dark.)

Scene 6

The School Playground

Adam, Rob and Jemma are standing talking together. Mark enters. As he walks past them, Rob sticks out his foot and Mark trips. Adam and Jemma start to laugh.

Jemma: Muslim-lover.

(Adam, Rob and Jemma walk off. Shaleem comes in and stands in front of Mark, looking him right in the eye.)

Shaleem: Mark, why are you doing this? Why are you trying to avoid me?

Mark: You saw what happened in class.

Shaleem: So?

Mark: If I sit with you, everyone will hate me.

Shaleem: So it's all right for them to hate *me*, then?

Mark: No! No, you don't get it ...

Shaleem: I get it all right. You're just a coward. You know they're wrong, but you won't stand up to them.

Mark: It's not like that.

Shaleem: Yes, it is. I thought you were my friend.

Mark: I am!

Shaleem: Friends don't turn their backs, Mark.

Mark: We can still be friends out of school.

Shaleem: No, we can't. Not if you won't stand up for me.

Mark: I'm not strong enough.

Shaleem:	So you're leaving me to face them on my own, are you?
Mark:	No ...

(Adam, Jemma and Rob come in. They walk over to Mark and Shaleem.)

Rob:	Hey, you. Corner-shop boy.
Mark:	Rob, not you too. I thought you were a mate.
Rob:	It's us or them, Mark. You can't be friends with the enemy.
Mark:	Shaleem's not the enemy.

Jemma:	There's a war on, Mark, or didn't you know?
Adam:	The war on terror.
Rob:	Wars have enemies.
Jemma:	Terrorists are the enemy.
Adam:	Muslims are terrorists.
Rob:	Shaleem's a Muslim.
Jemma:	That makes Shaleem the enemy.
Mark:	No, you've got it all wrong ...

(Adam goes right up to Mark and speaks to him, close up to his face.)

Adam: Don't get in my way, Mark. This isn't about you. Don't make yourself an enemy too.

(Adam, Rob and Jemma stand in a ring around Shaleem.)

Adam: This is about Shaleem.

Jemma: And people like him.

Rob: Muslims.

Shaleem: I've told you, being a Muslim doesn't make you a bad person. That's just crazy.

Adam: You calling me crazy?

Jemma: His dad's going to be in a wheelchair for the rest of his life.

Rob: Because of people like you.

Shaleem: They're not like me! Just because they have the same religion ...

Adam: But that's the problem, Shaleem.

Jemma: They have the same religion.

Rob: So they think like you.

Adam: And it's time we did something about it.

(Suddenly, Adam, Jemma and Rob all pile in on top of Shaleem, kicking and punching and yelling. For a short moment, Shaleem breaks free and shouts to Mark.)

Shaleem: Mark! Help me!

(Then Adam kicks Shaleem hard, and Shaleem goes down again. He is getting badly hurt. Mark takes a step towards them, but then he stops. They all freeze.)

(The stage goes dark.)

Stop! Read this first!

If the play is being read in the classroom ...

Should Mark step in to help Shaleem? Or should he walk away?

You decide!

If you think Mark should help his friend, go to Scene 7.

If you think Mark should stay out of it, go to Scene 8.

If the play is being performed ...

(Mark is standing alone on the stage, lit by a spotlight.   He turns to speak to the audience.)

Mark: I don't know what to do.

                   Help me choose.

(The lights are turned on so that the audience can be seen.)

Mark: It's your turn to become part

                   of the action. Think about

                   what you've just seen. I'm

                   going to ask you to choose

                   for me. Should I step in and

                   help? Or should I stay out of

it, like Adam said? Don't
just tell me to "do the right
thing". You know it's not as
simple as that. You tell me
what I should do, and then
we'll show you what
happens. So now – here's
your chance to vote. If you
think I should step in to help
my friend, put your hand up.

(Mark looks at the audience and counts the number of hands.)

Mark: OK. Now, if you think I
                   should stay well out of it, put
                   your hand up.

(Mark counts the new number of hands.)

Mark: OK. Thanks for making my
mind up for me. Now we'll
show you what my life is like
after the fight. Remember,
it was your choice.

*(The lights on the audience are turned down
again. If there were more votes for Mark to
step in and help Shaleem, now perform Scene
7. If there were more votes for Mark staying
out of the fight, perform Scene 8.)*

Scene 7

The School Playground

It is break time, and the playground is full of students. Some are kicking a football around, others are just standing and chatting.

(Mark is sitting on a bench, alone. His hand has a bandage on it. Rob walks past.)

Mark: Rob. Hey, Rob!

(Rob looks around to see if anyone is watching them. Rob then sits down on the bench next to Mark.)

Mark: You can't ignore me for ever.

Rob: Why did you do it, Mark?
            Adam told you to stay out of
            the fight.

Mark: I know. But I'm his mate,
            Rob. We've always been
            mates. I said we'd always be
            mates.

Rob: Things have changed.

Mark: No they haven't. He's still
            the same Shaleem. You used
            to get on fine with him.

Rob: That was before the bombs.
            We can't go back. Things
            are different now.

Mark: You're just going along with everyone else. All the people who turn their backs on me. You're just doing what they do. Can't you think for yourself?

Rob: I have to go along with them. It's easier than trying to stand up to them. You did, and look what happened to you. Two broken fingers and no friends.

Mark: I'd rather be on my own and right than with everyone else and wrong.

Rob: Don't be stupid, Mark. It's
              not about right and wrong.

(Adam and Jemma walk in, their arms linked together. Rob sees them, jumps up and walks up to them. Mark calls to Rob.)

Mark: Coward.

(Adam looks angry. He turns to Rob.)

Adam: Were you talking to that
              tosser?

Rob: No.

Jemma: Yes, you were. We saw you.

Rob: Just telling him what a git he
                is. That's all.

Adam: Well, just you make sure
                that's all it is. No one talks
                to him now. Got it?

Rob: Yeah, yeah, I got it.

Jemma: No one talks to him or the
                other one.

Rob: I know. I wasn't.

Adam: Right then.

(Adam, Jemma and Rob walk off. Adam looks
back at Mark as they go and spits on the

floor. Shaleem enters from the other side of the stage. He joins Mark on the bench, sitting down very slowly, as if it hurts him.)

Mark: How are the ribs?

Shaleem: They're all right. My dad says it was lucky they didn't break. And my nose has healed up OK. How about you?

Mark: I'll be OK. It's just all this crap at school.

Shaleem: It won't last for ever.

Mark: How do you know? It's only been two weeks and it already feels like for ever. Rob spoke to me today for the first time since the fight. He's the only one who has. I've got no mates.

Shaleem: You've got me.

Mark: Yeah ...

Shaleem: I owe you.

Mark: No, you don't.

Shaleem: If you hadn't stepped in when you did ...

Mark: Don't go on about it.

Shaleem: I could be dead. My dad says –

Mark: Oh, shut up about your bloody dad! I'm fed up of hearing how perfect he is all the time! Rub it in, why don't you?

Shaleem: I didn't mean to.

Mark: So your dad's a doctor. Well, so what? My dad's a lorry driver and you know what? He's a bloody good one too!

Shaleem: I'm sure he is …

Mark: And when I've got enough money saved up, I'm going to go live with him. So I can get away from my door-mat mum and her psycho boyfriend Dennis. You know what he did when Mum told him I stood up for you? He gave me a smack too – right on the side of the head. Called me all sorts of names. And Mum just stood there and watched. I'm not taking it any more.

Shaleem:	I'm sorry.
Mark:	You should be! It's all because of you! "I can fight my own battles," you said – and then you get yourself beaten up!
Shaleem:	You didn't have to come in and help.
Mark:	What was I supposed to do? "Help me, Mark, help me," you kept saying. Was I supposed to stand by and do nothing?
Shaleem:	I've said thank you.

Mark: Yeah, but is it enough, Shaleem? Was it really worth it?

Shaleem: What are you saying?

Mark: Because of you, the rest of the school won't speak to me any more. I get dog shit put in my locker. I get tripped on the way to class. My bag gets nicked and my mobile gets stamped on. All because I helped out a mate. And I got two broken fingers.

Shaleem: You did the right thing,
Mark.

Mark: Yeah? Funny, because that's
not how it feels.

(Mark stands up.)

Mark: It's like Rob said – it's not
about right and wrong.

Shaleem: Of course it is.

Mark: No, it isn't. It's about
staying alive. Getting
through. And I might have
you, but I haven't got anyone
else. Even my mum said she

didn't understand why I did what I did.

Shaleem: You're sorry you helped me.

Mark: You know what? You might be right.

Shaleem: We're still mates, aren't we?

Mark: I dunno. It's never going to be the same.

Shaleem: I'm sorry.

Mark: Yeah. Me too.

(The stage goes dark.)

Scene 8

The School Playground

It is break time, and the playground is full of students. Some are kicking a football around, others are just standing and chatting.

(Mark is sitting on a bench, alone. Rob walks past.)

Mark: Rob. Hey, Rob!

Rob: Oh, hey, Mark.

(Rob comes over and sits next to Mark on the bench.)

Rob: So, how you doing?

Mark: OK. I failed that test in Maths, though.

Rob: Oh, me too, me too! But hey, who cares?

Mark: Well ...

Rob: Think about it, who's going to need Maths after we leave school? We've got computers for all that stuff!

Mark: Yeah, you're right.

Rob: No one cares about Maths.

(Shaleem enters. He is walking slowly and with a limp.)

Rob: Apart from him, of course.

(Shaleem sees Mark and Rob, and stops.)

Rob: You're well out of that, mate. You did the right thing.

Mark: I didn't do anything.

Rob: That's what I mean. It wasn't your fight. Adam told you to stay out. If you'd jumped in to help him …

Mark: Yeah. It's just ... he was my friend. And he got hurt pretty bad.

Rob: That's not your fault.

(Shaleem walks over to them.)

Shaleem: Hey, Mark.

(Mark looks over at Rob and says nothing.)

Shaleem: Look, I know you don't want to be friends any more. I get it.

Rob: Yeah, and no one else wants to be friends either. So you might as well push off.

(Shaleem ignores Rob and talks to Mark again.)

Shaleem: I just wanted to say it's OK.
I don't want you to blame
yourself.

Rob: Why would he blame
himself? You're the one in
the crap.

Shaleem: My leg's healing up OK, and
my dad says my ribs will
stop hurting soon.
Everything else was just cuts
and bruises.

Rob: You were lucky.

Shaleem: You didn't want to help.

Rob: Why would he?

Shaleem: We were friends. I just wanted to say, any time you change your mind ...

(Mark looks at Shaleem for the first time. Just at that moment, Adam and Jemma walk in, their arms linked together. Adam is angry to see Shaleem.)

Adam: What are you doing here, scum?

Jemma: Get out of our way.

Adam: You're not fit to look at us,

                let alone speak.

Jemma: Tell him to get lost, Mark.

*(Shaleem looks at Mark. Mark looks at the
floor.)*

Mark: Yeah, that's right. We don't

                want you here. Get lost.

(Shaleem nods and walks off.)

Adam: You told him.

Jemma: Good work, Mark.

(Rob slaps Mark on the back.)

Rob: Did you see his face!

(Mark doesn't look happy.)

Mark: Yeah.

Adam: Come on. We're bunking the last lesson and going into town. Jemma's got a mate who can get us free beer.

(Rob stands up.)

Rob: Yeah! Come on, Mark.

(Adam and Jemma walk off. Mark gets up but then stands still. He looks toward the other side of the stage, where Shaleem went. Rob seems to know what Mark's thinking.)

Rob: You're better off without him, mate. Honest.

Mark: I guess.

Rob: Look at it this way – if you were still mates with him, you couldn't be mates with us.

(Rob slaps Mark on the back in a friendly way.)

Rob: It's a no-brainer. Hurry up, or you'll get left behind.

(Rob runs off after Adam and Jemma. Mark stands there for a moment longer.)

Mark: Yeah. Free beer. Right.

(Again, Mark looks towards Shaleem's side of the stage. It is clear he doesn't want to go with Rob, but then he shakes his head.)

Mark: A no-brainer. Yeah.

(Mark goes off the same way Rob went. The stage goes dark.)